ENCORE!

JOHN HARLE

CHESTER MUSIC

1   Matthew's Song

John Harle

* In bb. 31–47 the music shown is a suggested line and can be played if the player does not want to improvise.

† Note to the saxophone player: if you've never improvised before start very slowly, and play each of the notes in the scale and see how they sound with the accompaniment and gradually build up to play a few of them together – think of rhythms that sound right for the music and use the scale notes to help you construct lines or phrases.

2   The Fool

Andy Sheppard and Steve Lodder

* See note on p.3

2 The Fool

Andy Sheppard and Steve Lodder

* See note on p.3

3 Blues for Marguerite

Theme from 'Comrade Lady' (Channel 4 Films)

John Harle

* Improvise during the repeat of bb. 21–36 using the chords shown; alternatively repeat the line shown for these bars.

Written by John Harle

4 Tender is the Night

Nicole's Theme

Richard Rodney Bennett
Arranged by John Harle
and Hywel Davies

5 Tender is the Night
Rosemary's Waltz

Richard Rodney Bennett
Arranged by John Harle
and Hywel Davies

6 Flow My Teares (Lachrimae)

Recorded on 'John Harle's Saxophone Songbook' (Unicorn-Kanchana Records)

John Dowland
(Second Booke of Songs or Ayres, 1600)
Arranged by John Harle and Steve Lodder

6 Flow My Teares (Lachrimae)

Recorded on 'John Harle's Saxophone Songbook' (Unicorn-Kanchana Records)

John Dowland
(Second Booke of Songs or Ayres, 1600)
Arranged by John Harle and Steve Lodder

7 Je te veux

Erik Satie
Arranged by John Harle
and Hywel Davies

8 Novello Blues

From 'Play the Saxophone With John Harle' video (Novello)

John Harle
Piano arrangement by
Hywel Davies

* 'Swung' quavers (♩♩ = ♩♪) throughout.

Written by John Harle

9   Qui n'aroit autre deport

Recorded on 'John Harle's Saxophone Songbook' (Unicorn-Kanchana Records)

Guillaume de Machaut
Arranged by John Harle
and Steve Lodder

10 Hum Drum

From 'Play the Saxophone With John Harle' video (Novello)

John Harle
Piano arrangement by
Hywel Davies

11   Lost and Found

Michael Nyman
Arranged by John Harle
and Hywel Davies

12   Cradle Song

John Harle

* Improvise and repeat *ad lib.* for ending

* If you've never improvised before, start by playing the following two scales over the piano chords and see if you can use your imagination to play something else, using these notes:

** Pause on 1st beat after improvisation.

© 1993 PolyGram Music Publishing Ltd. International Copyright Secured. All Rights Reserved.

6/08(165968)
Printed in England

CONTENTS

ENCORE!

JOHN
HARLE

CHESTER MUSIC

Matthew's Song, **Novello Blues** and **Hum Drum**
are all featured on the educational video
Play the Saxophone with John Harle *(NOV 640003)*
available from Music Sales Limited.

Cover photograph by Johnny Greig.

This book © Copyright 1996 Chester Music.
Order No. CH 61090
ISBN 0-7119-5154-3

Music processed by Barnes Music Engraving.
Printed and bound in Great Britain

Exclusive distributors:
Music Sales Limited, Newmarket Road,
Bury St Edmunds, Suffolk IP33 3YB.
All rights reserved.

CONTENTS

1 Matthew's Song

John Harle

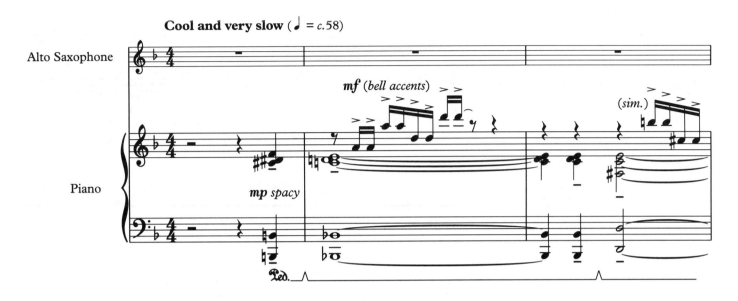

* Embellish piano part if desired.

* In bb. 31–47 the music shown for the saxophone is a suggested line and can be played if the player does not want to improvise.

** The pianist can 'fill out' the piano part using the chords shown.

† Note to the saxophone player: if you've never improvised before start very slowly, and play each of the notes in the scale and see how they sound with the accompaniment and gradually build up to play a few of them together – think of rhythms that sound right for the music and use the scale notes to help you construct lines or phrases.

2 The Fool

Andy Sheppard and Steve Lodder

3 Blues for Marguerite

Theme from 'Comrade Lady' (Channel 4 Films)

John Harle

* Improvise during the repeat of bb. 21–36 using the chords shown; alternatively repeat the line shown for these bars.

4 Tender is the Night

Nicole's Theme

Richard Rodney Bennett
Arranged by John Harle
and Hywel Davies

5 Tender is the Night

Rosemary's Waltz

Richard Rodney Bennett
Arranged by John Harle
and Hywel Davies

6 Flow My Teares (Lachrimae)

Recorded on 'John Harle's Saxophone Songbook' (Unicorn-Kanchana Records)

John Dowland
(Second Booke of Songs or Ayres, 1600)
Arranged by John Harle and Steve Lodder

7 Je te veux

Erik Satie
Arranged by John Harle
and Hywel Davies

2nd time **to Coda** ⊕

8 Novello Blues

From 'Play the Saxophone With John Harle' video (Novello)

John Harle
Piano arrangement by
Hywel Davies

* 'Swung' quavers (♩♩ = ♩³♩) throughout.

Written by John Harle

9 Qui n'aroit autre deport

Recorded on 'John Harle's Saxophone Songbook' (Unicorn-Kanchana Records)

Guillaume de Machaut
Arranged by John Harle
and Steve Lodder

10 Hum Drum

From 'Play the Saxophone With John Harle' video (Novello)

John Harle
Piano arrangement
by Hywel Davies

11 Lost and Found

Michael Nyman
Arranged by John Harle
and Hywel Davies

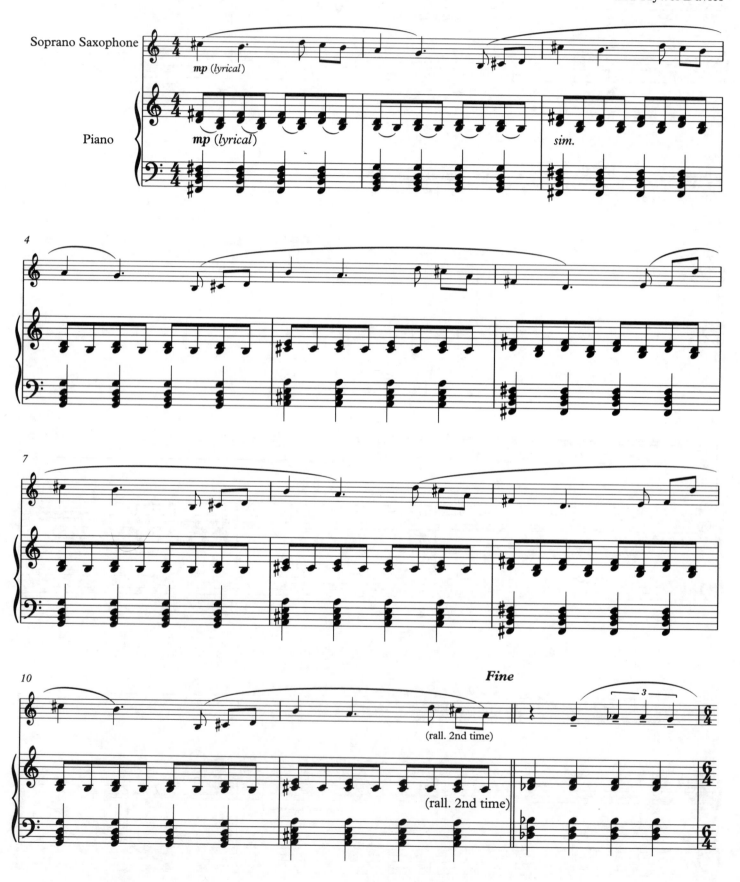

12 Cradle Song

John Harle

* Improvise and repeat *ad lib.* for ending

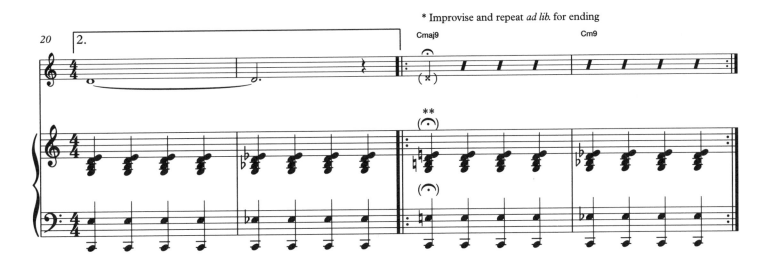

* If you've never improvised before, start by playing the following two scales over the piano chords and see if you can use your imagination to play something else, using these notes:

** Pause on 1st beat after improvisation.

6/08(165968)
Printed in England